The Nativity Story

Written by Lisa Regan

Brown Watson
ENGLAND

First published 2016 by Brown Watson
The Old Mill, 76 Fleckney Road
Kibworth Beauchamp
Leicestershire LE8 0HG
ISBN: 978-0-7097-2387-5
© 2016 Brown Watson, England
Printed in Malaysia

An ordinary young woman called Mary lived in the town of Nazareth, in a place called Judea. She was going to be married to a carpenter called Joseph.

Mary was extremely surprised when an angel visited her. 'God has blessed you,' said the Angel Gabriel. 'You will have a baby, the Son of God, and will call him Jesus.'

Joseph was worried about the news. He wondered if they shouldn't get married. An angel appeared, and told him to go ahead with the wedding.

Soon after, Mary and Joseph set off on a journey to Bethlehem. Everyone had been ordered to go to the town where they were born, so they could pay their taxes and be counted.

Mary was close to giving birth by now, and the journey was long and tiring. She travelled on a donkey through the dry and dusty land. They travelled slowly over the hills of Galilee and towards the town.

Finally, they arrived in Bethlehem. It was full of crowds of people who also had to pay their taxes. Mary and Joseph tried to find a room where they could stay for the night.

All the rooms were full, but a kind innkeeper
said they could share the stable with his animals.
It was warm and dry, but a bit smelly.
That is where Mary had her baby.

They wrapped the baby Jesus in clean cloth called swaddling, and laid him in a manger full of hay.

It was an unusual place to find the Son of God! The animals all watched him sleep peacefully.

Close by, a group of shepherds sat in the hills, keeping their sheep safe through the night. A bright light appeared, and an angel spoke to them. At first, they were frightened.

'I have great news!' called the angel. 'The Son of God has been born, and is lying in a manger in Bethlehem. You should visit him and give thanks to God!'

More angels appeared and lit up the night sky.
'Glory to God and peace to everyone!' they sang.

The shepherds travelled to Bethlehem to visit the Son of God. Sure enough, he was in a stable, surrounded by animals. The shepherds told everyone in the town what had happened.

Far away, some Wise Men who studied the
night skies saw a new star shining brightly.
'This means that a king is born!' they exclaimed.
'We must travel to find him.'

The Wise Men followed the bright star all the way to the stable. They went inside, where they knelt by the manger and worshipped Jesus.

They gave expensive gifts to the baby and His parents. They gave Him gold, and sweet smelling oils called frankincense and myrrh.

An angel appeared in the Wise Men's dreams.
He warned them about an evil king called Herod.
Herod didn't want there to be a new king.

An angel also gave Joseph a warning about Herod.
The angel told Joseph they must escape from
Bethlehem at once.

Joseph took Mary and Jesus away to Egypt where they would be safe. Jesus grew into a young man who told everyone about God and how people should be kind to each other.